Ideal School Supply Company   Grades 4-6

THINK ABOUT IT!
SCIENCE PROBLEMS OF THE DAY

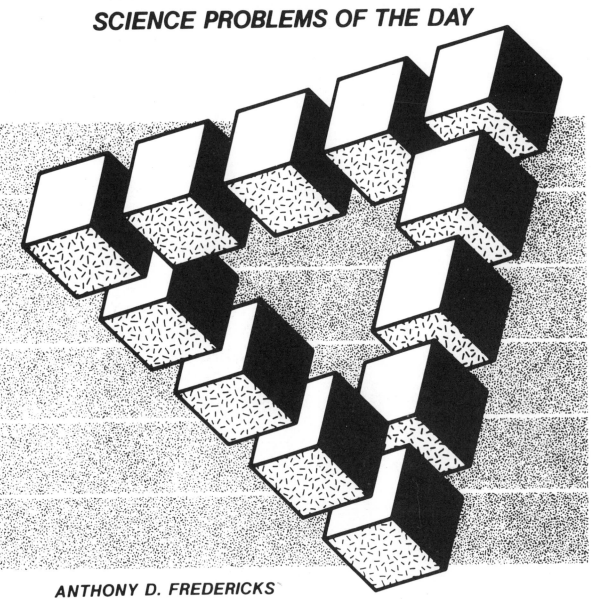

ANTHONY D. FREDERICKS

THINK ABOUT IT!
SCIENCE PROBLEMS OF THE DAY

Technical art by Huey Lee

.

DEDICATION

To three exemplary colleagues and great friends—Brian Glandon, Bonnie Blake-Kline, and Dean Cheesebrough.

Ideal School Supply Company • Alsip, Illinois • 60482

Printed in U.S.A.

ISBN: 1-56451-063-8

5 6 7 8 9 10. 9 6

Notes to the Teacher

Think About It! Science Problems of the Day presents a collection of problems focusing on the life sciences, earth and space sciences, and physical sciences. These problems are intended for students in grades 4–6, but would also be appropriate for gifted students in grade 3.

Think About It! Science Problems of the Day is designed to motivate students to use their science knowledge in real-life situations and explorations. The thought-provoking experiences rouse students' curiosity and help them develop an appreciation for the mysteries and marvels of the scientific world around them.

This binder contains 180 Daily Problems (one for each day, Monday through Friday, for 36 weeks), plus 36 Weekly Challenge problems. The content of the problems is as follows:

> Monday — Life Sciences
> Tuesday — Earth and Space Sciences
> Wednesday — Physical Sciences
> Thursday — Life Sciences
> Friday — Earth and Space Sciences

The Weekly Challenges present information and problems related to all of these sciences, giving students a well-rounded approach to scientific discoveries and inquiry.

It is suggested that you duplicate the Daily Problems for each of your students. You may want to assemble the problems in notebooks and allow the students to work on them throughout the school year. Or, you may want to post the Problem of the Day on the bulletin board and have students work on it as soon as they arrive at class or when they have some free time during the day. Another option would be to assign one problem a day as homework to be completed by the following day. Plan some time each day for students to discuss their solutions to the previous day's problem.

To complete the Weekly Challenges, students will have to do some independent investigation, using various types of reference materials, such as encyclopedias, science dictionaries, and star maps. These activities challenge students to assemble data, interpret information, and organize their thoughts. You may wish to post a Weekly Challenge on the bulletin board at the beginning of each week, and provide many opportunities throughout the week for students to work on the problem. Another option would be to distribute the Weekly Challenges as homework assignments. Be sure to plan time at the end of each week to discuss and share students' findings. As the year progresses, students may wish to gather their completed Weekly Challenges together into notebook collections, along with other classroom science work.

It is recommended that students work together in pairs or small groups on the problems. Cooperative problem-solving will give students the opportunity to help one another look at problems in a variety of ways, and to use the vocabulary of science as they gather data and work out the problem solutions together.

Many of the problems in this book are open-ended and lend themselves to further investigation. Encourage students to extend their research on those problems, or to create new weekly challenges and share them with the other students.

Solutions to the Daily Problems and Weekly Challenges are presented at the end of the book. Although only one solution may be given for a particular problem, there may well be other solutions that would satisfy the conditions of the problem. All answers should be discussed, and differing solutions should be encouraged and commended. For some of the Weekly Challenges, many solutions are possible, because students' answers will depend in part on their prior experience and knowledge. In other words, the Challenges allow students to record many different answers, rather than a single correct answer. When answers differ in some respect from those suggested in the Solution Key, encourage students to discuss how they arrived at their solutions or to give a rationale for selecting a particular solution. Helping students understand that science is not a static subject will be an important byproduct of these activities.

Monday ✓

Which one of these statements is not true?

1. Alligators live in swamps.
2. Alligators eat frogs.
3. Alligators are amphibians.
4. Alligators lay eggs.

Tuesday ✓

Unscramble each word. Which words name fossil fuels?

lio   odow   sag   loca

Wednesday ✓

I make plant roots grow down. I keep things from falling off the Earth. I make balls bounce. What am I?

Thursday

Fill in the puzzle, using only words that identify types of animal shelters.

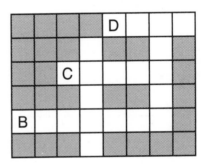

Friday ✓

I grew in a cave, but I'm not alive. I began as water and minerals, but now I am solid. I grow upwards, but I never see the sky. What am I?

Weekly Challenge

Animals have an interesting variety of names. A sheep is not just a sheep! A baby sheep is called a *lamb*, a female sheep is called a *ewe*, a male sheep is called a *ram*, and a group of sheep is called a *drove* or *flock*.

Use the clues given in the table, and fill in the missing names.

	Name of Animal	Name of Young	Name of Female	Name of Male	Name of Group	Where Do They Live?
1	sheep	lamb	ewe	ram	drove/flock	fold/pen
2			cow		pod/gam	ocean
3	bear					den
4		chick/peep	hen			
5		foal/colt			herd/team	
6			tigress			
7	lion					savanna
8		leveret	doe			
9	quail					
10		piglet				pen/sty

THINK ABOUT IT! Science Problems of the Day

Monday ✓

What is the largest organ human beings have?

Tuesday

A cup of coffee, a 10-gallon aquarium, and a bottle of ginger ale were on the same table. On which container was there the greatest amount of air pressure?

Wednesday

Richard bought $1\frac{3}{4}$ pounds of ice cream. How many grams of ice cream did he have?

Thursday

I am an important body tissue. I transmit messages throughout the body, particularly to the brain. You know I work whenever you scratch your finger. What am I?

Friday ✓

Where can light travel, but not sound?

Weekly Challenge

There are over a million different kinds of insects living on Earth. Imagine being an entomologist and trying to decide which insects to study! You will have to do some research on insects to answer the following questions about unusual members of the insect world.

1 Which insects have dramatic ways of signaling one another?

2 Which kind of caterpillar has a strange way of moving from the place where it sleeps to the place where it eats?

3 What beetle looks like a rhinoceros, and where is it found?

4 What are some of the largest moths in the world, and how wide are their wingspans?

5 What is one of the largest bees in the world, found only on one island?

6 What kind of beetle is 4 inches long, and where is it found?

7 What is unusual about the greenfly?

8 What is unusual about the way the hoverfly moves?

9 What kind of insect has a total life span of only 3 to 4 hours?

10 What female insect usually kills and eats her mate?

   THINK ABOUT IT! Science Problems of the Day   © 1993 Ideal School Supply Company

Monday

I can live in both fresh water and salt water. When full grown, I migrate long distances to my place of birth. What am I?

Tuesday ✓

How many continents are there on Earth? How many of them are completely surrounded by water?

Wednesday ✓

I do not have shape or volume. You cannot see me, but I fill any container in which I am placed. I have weight, but you cannot hold me. What am I?

Thursday

Unscramble each word. Which word names something that is not a nut?

necap   tenpau   lawtun   wacseh

Friday

Javier lives in an area where there is a lot of igneous rock. What is probably nearby?

Weekly Challenge

The word *symmetry* indicates balance. An object may have *line symmetry*, which is also called *mirror symmetry*. If you divide the object in half with a line, the half on one side of the line is the *mirror image* of the half on the other side of the line. If you place a mirror on the line, the one half plus its reflection in the mirror will look like the whole object.

What capital letters have line symmetry? Use a mirror to test each letter of the alphabet. If the line of symmetry runs from top to bottom, the letter has vertical symmetry. If the line runs from side to side, the letter has horizontal symmetry. Some letters may have both kinds of symmetry, and some may have neither. Record the results of your test.

A   B   C   D   E   F   G   H   I   J   K   L   M

N   O   P   Q   R   S   T   U   V   W   X   Y   Z

Vertical	Horizontal	Both	Neither
A	B		

Many living organisms have symmetry, even though it is seldom perfect symmetry. Which of the following organisms have line symmetry, and what kind?

	Vertical	Horizontal	Both	Neither
human	✔			
dog				
bird				
clam				
amoeba				
spider				
frog				

 THINK ABOUT IT! Science Problems of the Day

Monday ✓

My body is covered with bony plates, but I am a fish. I am male, but I take care of all my young. I can swim, but I prefer to be carried by ocean currents. I look like a familiar land animal. What am I?

Tuesday ✓

Name a landform that is created by living organisms. These organisms are invertebrates.

Wednesday ✓

Tammy's jacket absorbs all of the light that strikes it. What color is it? Is it safe for her to wear it when she rides her bicycle at night?

Thursday ✓

Unscramble each word. Which words name mammals?

ravebe   noplidh   canroco   lisan

Friday ✓

I hold the celestial record for the fastest revolution around this solar system's largest star. What am I?

Weekly Challenge

Some animals are concealed from their predators by protective coloration, because they are naturally the same color as their surroundings. Some animals resemble other more dangerous or distasteful animals in color. Other animals actually change their color to match their surroundings.

Describe how these animals use coloration to protect or conceal themselves.

1 The snowshoe hare and the arctic fox _____

_____

2 The king snake _____

_____

3 The sphinx moth _____

_____

4 The monarch butterfly _____

_____

5 The leaf butterfly _____

_____

6 The ptarmigan _____

_____

7 The katydid _____

_____

8 The walking stick _____

_____

9 The stingray _____

_____

10 The robber fly _____

_____

THINK ABOUT IT! Science Problems of the Day   © 1993 Ideal School Supply Company

Monday

I am one of the longest plants in the world. Sometimes I am green, sometimes I am brown. Sometimes I have roots, sometimes I don't. Part of me is used in the manufacture of ice cream. What am I?

Tuesday

Unscramble each word. Which word names something that burns up in the Earth's atmosphere?

roteem   arts   tocem   ristadeo

Wednesday

Which of these rates of speed is the fastest?

40 km/h   28 mi/h   19 knots/h

Thursday

Give one example of each kind of animal.
1. Herbivore —
2. Carnivore —
3. Omnivore —

Friday ✓

I can travel where there are no molecules, but never through a brick. I can travel through space, but never around a corner. What am I?

Weekly Challenge

Light reflection may be regular or scattered and diffused. This depends on the nature of the surface the light is striking.

Try doing an experiment on light reflection. First collect these objects:

flashlight	foil	black paper	yellow paper
glass object	mirror	white paper	white shirt

Do your experiment in a dark area. Fasten each object against a wall, and then shine the light on it. Test each of the following objects, and number them in order from brightest to least bright. The brightest is a regular reflection, while the least bright is a diffused reflection.

_____ white paper, smooth

_____ dull side of foil, smooth

_____ dull side of foil, wrinkled

_____ shiny side of foil, smooth

_____ shiny side of foil, wrinkled

_____ mirror

_____ white shirt

_____ black paper

_____ glass object

_____ yellow paper

_____ white paper, wrinkled

THINK ABOUT IT! Science Problems of the Day

Monday

Unscramble each word. Which words name reptiles?

lertut   kasen   gofr   ridzal   dorclecoi

Tuesday

Candy sees this weather symbol in the newspaper.
What does it mean?

Wednesday ✓

What force will stop the ski?

Thursday ✓

I have roots and a stem, but I do not produce a flower, or fruit, or seeds. I
have no chlorophyl to make my own food, so I do not need sunlight. I
have gills that produce spores. I live in forests and woods. What am I?

Friday

Terry weighs 2016 ounces on Earth. How much would she weigh on
the moon?

Weekly Challenge

The words missing from the table are listed below. Write each word in its correct space, and then fill in any missing information.

	System in the Human Body	Components	What Does the System Do?
1	circulatory	heart, blood, vessels	carries food and oxygen to body parts
2	muscular		moves body parts
3			gets rid of body wastes
4			protects body organs
5			controls muscles and organs; thinking and learning
6		stomach, intestines	
7	endocrine		
8		lungs	

brain	thyroid glands	respiratory
pituitary gland	ribs	skeletal
skull	ligaments	excretory
muscles	skin	nervous
lungs	adrenal glands	digestive
spinal cord	bones in limbs	
spinal column	large intestine	
tendons		

Monday

Fill in the puzzle, using only the names of parts of the human eye.

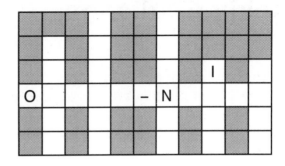

Tuesday ✓

When I am hot, I am a liquid. When I am cool, I am a solid. I can make mountains and destroy towns. I spend most of my time underground. What am I?

Wednesday

Marty poured hot water into his cup and then let it cool off. What was happening to the particles of matter in the cup as the water cooled?

Thursday ✓

Pat ties a swing to a branch of an oak tree. The seat of the swing is 22 inches from the ground. If the tree grows 8 inches a year, how far off the ground will the swing seat be in $5\frac{1}{2}$ years?

Friday

What is a guyot?

Weekly Challenge

The surface of the Earth contains a wonderful variety of rocks. One kind of rock floats! Another kind is so hard that it cuts glass.

Fill in the empty spaces of the table.

	Kind of Rock	Major Classification	Characteristics (Appearance/Hardness/etc.)	How Was It Formed?
1	granite	igneous	large crystals	slowly cooling lava
2	shale		fine-grained	sediments of mud/clay/silt built up over time
3			very hard; originally sandstone	great heat, great pressure
4	gneiss		salt and pepper appearance	
5	sandstone	sedimentary		
6		igneous	gray; floats on water	rapidly cooling lava
7	diamond	metamorphic		
8		metamorphic	white	
9	limestone	sedimentary		sediments of sand built up over time
10			black, glassy	rapidly cooling lava

Monday

Name one land animal, one ocean animal, and one air animal that migrate.

Tuesday ✓

Which ocean has an area greater than that of all the continents combined?

Wednesday

Unscramble each word. Which word tells what copper is?

telneme   nopdumoc   mota   lelcomue

Thursday ✓

Lots of animals eat plants in order to survive. But sometimes it's the other way around. Give two examples of carnivorous plants, and tell how their leaves are specially designed to trap food.

Friday

Nikki lives near the deepest ocean trench in the world. What country does she live in?

Weekly Challenge

Animals have many different types of "ears," and they also exhibit different hearing abilities.

1 "Ears" or sound receivers are not located in the same place on all animals. What animals have sound receivers in these locations?

On their legs _____

_____

On the sides of their body _____

_____

On the sides of their head _____

_____

On their antennae _____

_____

2 Some animals have unusual "ears." What kinds of sound receivers do these animals have?

Fish _____

Frogs _____

3 Humans can hear sound vibrations in the range of 20–20,000 cycles per second. What animals can hear the following sound vibrations?

Ultrasonic (above 20,000 cycles per second) _____

Subsonic (below 20 cycles per second) _____

4 Some animals use sound and hearing in unique ways. What animals use these patterns of sound?

Echo location _____

Sonar _____

THINK ABOUT IT! Science Problems of the Day

Monday

I am a structure that protects objects inside of me. I am always used for support, and am sometimes made of cartilage. Calcium is important to my growth. What am I?

Tuesday

Fill in the puzzle, using the names of states (in the U.S.A.) in which volcanoes are located.

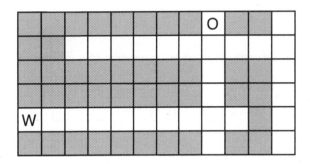

Wednesday

What chemical compound covers over two thirds of the Earth's surface?

Thursday

Unscramble each word. Which words name methods of pollination?

tarew   citsens   diwn   risdb   usn

Friday ✓

I can be three different states of matter, but not at the same time. I am necessary for life, but I can also destroy life. I can be under your feet, around your body, or over your head. What am I?

Weekly Challenge

What forces would be involved if you did these activities? Write **yes** or **no** in each column.

		Friction	Magnetism	Electricity	Gravity
1	ride a bicycle	yes	no	no	yes
2	ski down a hill				
3	shine a flashlight				
4	operate a model train				
5	turn on a television set				
6	push a car out of a pile of snow				
7	walk on the moon				
8	make a telephone call				
9	brush your teeth				
10	use a computer				

Can you think of some activities that would involve all four forces?

   THINK ABOUT IT! Science Problems of the Day   © 1993 Ideal School Supply Company

Monday ✓

The three smallest bones in the human body are located in the middle ear. What are they called, and what do they do?

Tuesday

I am an area that contains oxygen, nitrogen, and water. I am the layer of the atmosphere nearest to the surface of the Earth. Storms and other weather conditions are very much a part of me. What am I?

Wednesday

I am formed by heat and pressure in metamorphic rock. I am made up of carbon atoms. I can separate the colors of the spectrum like a prism. I am so hard that I can cut glass. What am I?

Thursday

Unscramble each word. Which word names something that is not a carbohydrate?

ceettul   ceri   lecare   derab   oottap

Friday

Claire is interested in measuring the magnitude of earthquakes. What instrument would she use?

Weekly Challenge

Animals can be grouped or classified in many different ways. They can be grouped according to their skin coverings, their feeding habits, their body structures, and so on.

How many different groups or categories can you think of that would each include at least five of these animals? Name the animals that belong in each category.

kangaroo	toad	turtle	butterfly	elephant
trout	vulture	porcupine	rabbit	bear

Category 1: _Animals that hunt for food during the day (diurnal)_

kangaroo	turtle	rabbit	butterfly
elephant	vulture	bear	trout

Category 2: _____

Category 3: _____

Category 4: _____

Category 5: _____

THINK ABOUT IT! Science Problems of the Day   © 1993 Ideal School Supply Company

Monday

Carrie, 14 years old, broke four bones in her left foot and two ribs when she fell off a scaffold. How many bones in her body remained unbroken?

Tuesday

Jenny is at the top of Mt. Washington in New Hampshire. Marcia is two-thirds the way up to the top of Mt. McKinley in Alaska. Who is experiencing greater air pressure?

Wednesday ✓

What part of a carrot plant could be considered a wedge?

Thursday

Unscramble each word. Which word names the edible part of an onion plant?

mets   troo   klats   vesale

Friday ✓

How many stars form the bowl of the Big Dipper?

Weekly Challenge

Which body of water is described by each set of clues?

1 This ocean surrounds the North Pole. It is frozen most of the year, and contains many icebergs. Which ocean is it?

_____

2 This is the largest body of water on Earth. It lies between Asia and North and South America, and has numerous volcanoes in it. Which ocean is it?

_____

3 This sea is north of South America. Its very warm waters are the origin of the Gulf Stream. Which body of water is it?

_____

4 This ocean is bordered by Saudi Arabia and Africa, and was the location of many Biblical stories. Its temperature is very warm. Which ocean is it?

_____

5 Mostly located in the Southern Hemisphere, this body of water lies between Africa and Asia. It is the second largest ocean on Earth. Which ocean is it?

_____

6 This ocean is known for violent storms. Located around Antarctica, it is inhabited by penguins and seals. Which ocean is it?

_____

7 At one time, this ocean was thought to be the edge of the world. It is crisscrossed by many communication cables. It is located within latitude N 60° to S 65° and longitude W 75° to E 5°. Which ocean is it?

_____

8 The United States and Mexico border this rich fishing area. Hurricanes occur frequently every year on this body of water. Which one is it?

_____

9 Bordered by Europe and Africa, this is the largest enclosed sea on Earth. The first trade routes were established on this body of water many centuries ago. What is it?

_____

    THINK ABOUT IT! Science Problems of the Day   © 1993 Ideal School Supply Company

Monday

Arnold grows three different edible taproots in his garden. What could they be?

Tuesday

Fill in the puzzle, using only words having to do with water vapor.

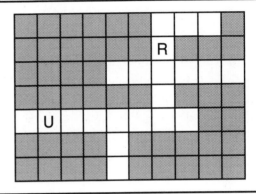

Wednesday

What instrument could you use to measure the force of gravity on an object?

Thursday

During photosynthesis, plants produce something that humans need for survival. What is it?

Friday ✓

I am a large mass of frozen water. I can move rocks and boulders. I move very slowly, but I cause great changes on Earth. What am I?

Weekly Challenge

In our everyday lives, we use heat energy, water energy, electric energy, and energy from fossil fuels such as coal and gas.

Decide what kind of energy is being used or conserved in each situation. Write U if the energy is being used; write C if the energy is being conserved. In some activities, one kind of energy may be used while another kind is being conserved.

	Activity	Heat	Water	Electric	Fossil Fuels
1	an egg boiling	U		U	U
2	a dam in operation				
3	a water heater left on overnight				
4	someone riding a bicycle to school or to work				
5	someone traveling by train				
6	solar panels being used to heat rooms				
7	a refrigerator door being opened				
8	an insulated attic				
9	someone taking short showers				
10	a home thermostat set at 68° F				

Monday

Name three food sources of vitamin D. Why does your body need that vitamin?

Tuesday

How many planets have rings?

Wednesday

Fill in the puzzle, using only words related to sound.

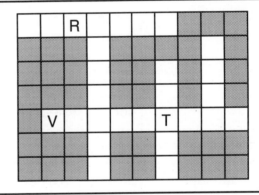

Thursday ✓

A tarantula is using its two front legs to hold a fly. How many legs is it not using?

Friday

Halley's Comet was seen twice in the 20th Century. Which sighting was closer to your birthday?

Weekly Challenge

In each ecological community, some animals are predators, some are prey, and some are both predators and prey.

For each community, list the animals that are predators and the animals that are prey.

	Community	Animals			Predator	Prey
1	desert	snake rodents grubs mouse	fly beetle woodpecker lizard			
2	forest	mouse anteater rat wolf ants lion	hawk owl hare salmon bobcat weasel	deer bear rabbit antelope		
3	ocean/lake	shark perch frog bass	pelican minnows nymph trout			
4	salt marsh	spider crab heron moth hawk	clam tern minnow duck grasshopper			

THINK ABOUT IT! Science Problems of the Day

Monday

Name three essential nutrients for your body.

Tuesday

Unscramble each word. One word names something that includes all of the others. Which word is it?

resdoita   sivrenue   lagyax   rolas mysset

Wednesday

Bernie and Bianca are on a seesaw. Bernie weighs 75 pounds and Bianca weighs 60 pounds. If the seesaw is balanced evenly, who is sitting closer to the fulcrum?

Thursday

Name an edible tuber.

Friday

Lois is watching a series of cumulus clouds form on the horizon. What type of weather will she probably experience in the next few hours?

Weekly Challenge

Write the missing information in the table of constellations and stars.

	Constellation	Popular Name	Brightest Star	Best Seen During Which Season?
1	Taurus	Bull	Aldebaran	winter
2		Chariot Driver	Capella	fall
3	Cepheus		none	all seasons
4			Betelgeuse	winter
5			Polaris	all seasons
6	Canis Major			
7	Cassiopeia			
8	Scorpius		Antares	
9	Leo	Lion		

   THINK ABOUT IT! Science Problems of the Day   © 1993 Ideal School Supply Company

Monday

What are three food sources of vitamin C? Why is this vitamin important for your body?

Tuesday

Unscramble each word. Which words name grassland regions?

tedres   ripaei   petsep   letdv

Wednesday

Which situation will require the most force?

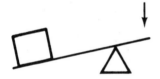 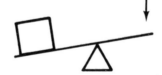 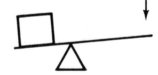

Thursday

Name two animals that go through metamorphosis.

Friday

How long would it take a beam of light to travel from Venus to Mars?

Weekly Challenge

Illustrate the phases of the moon by coloring in the circles. Draw arrows between the circles to show the order in which these phases are seen on Earth. Write one of these names next to each circle.

Last Quarter   Waxing Crescent   Full Moon   Waning Crescent

First Quarter   Waning Gibbous   Waxing Gibbous

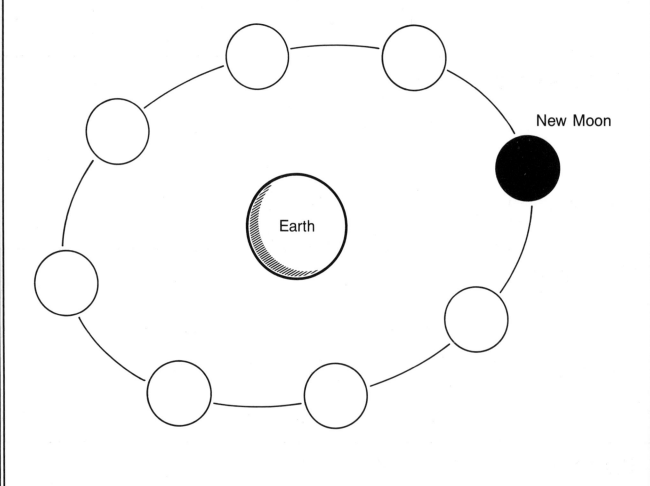

THINK ABOUT IT! Science Problems of the Day   © 1993 Ideal School Supply Company

Monday

Unscramble each word. Which words tell what all seeds must have for germination?

mawhtr   ria   losi   rawet   trefriizle

Tuesday

Fill in the puzzle, using only words that describe forms of precipitation.

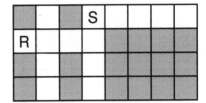

Wednesday

Which situation will require the least force?

  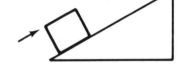

Thursday

I have gills for breathing under water. I have lungs for breathing on land. What am I?

Friday

Which would have the greatest weight?

1. 3 ounces of iron on Earth
2. 3 pounds of pencils on the moon
3. $\frac{1}{2000}$ of a ton of coffee on Earth

Weekly Challenge

A food chain illustrates how energy passes from one organism to another.

In each food chain, circle the name of the plant or animal that does not belong in it. Explain why it doesn't belong in that chain.

	Food Chain	Why Doesn't It Belong?
1	wolf → rabbit → (grasshopper) → lettuce	Rabbits don't eat grasshoppers.
2	hawk → rabbit → snake → mouse → seed	
3	bear → turtle → berries	
4	deer → snake → rodents → roots	
5	human → dolphin → tuna → anchovy	
6	frog → butterfly → grasshopper → grass	
7	weasel → rattlesnake → mouse → sunflower seeds	
8	coyote → hawk → mice → cactus	
9	human → deer → trout → worm	

Monday

Fill in the puzzle, using only
words that describe parts of a plant.

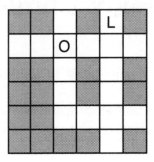

Tuesday

Which of the following statements is not true?

1. There are many craters on the moon's surface.
2. There are many mountains and hills on the moon.
3. Erosion has created large numbers of valleys on the surface of the moon.
4. The face of the moon has large, flat plains.

Wednesday

How much faster does sound travel through water than through air in
one second?

Thursday

Unscramble each word. Which words name parts of flowers?

fela   aplet   matnes   uveol   tiplis

Friday

During a certain part of the day, the waters off the west coast of the
United States are at right angles to the moon. What kind of tide is
occurring in San Francisco Bay at that time?

Weekly Challenge

Try to listen to as many of these musical instruments as you can.

Tell what produces the sound in each instrument. Then describe the pitch and frequency of vibrations.

	Musical Instrument	What Produces the Sound?	Pitch (High/Low)	Frequency (Fast/Slow)
1	soprano voice	vocal cords	high	fast
2	guitar			
3	kettle drum			
4	alto voice			
5	alto saxophone			
6	violin			
7	trumpet			
8	flute			
9	clarinet			
10	bass fiddle			
11	cello			
12	xylophone			

Monday

If you want to decrease the amount of $C_6H_{12}O_6$ in your diet, what foods should you decrease?

Tuesday

Unscramble each word. On which planet would you weigh less than you do on Earth?

tanrus   sevun   pentuen   pejtiur

Wednesday

Clarissa is standing at the bottom of a canyon, shouting at a canyon wall that is 4360 feet away. How long will it take for the sound to come back to her as an echo?

Thursday

What makes fireflies and glowworms luminescent?

Friday

Charlie notes that one part of tomorrow's weather report predicts wind speeds of 12 knots. What instrument will be used to measure that?

Weekly Challenge

1 How many miles away from the sun is each of these planets?

Mercury	Venus	Earth	Mars	Jupiter

2 What is the outside temperature where you are now? _____ F

Approximately how many times hotter than that would the temperature be on each of these planets?

Mercury	Venus	Neptune

Approximately how many times colder than that would the temperature be on each of these planets?

Saturn	Uranus	Mars

3 If a new day began on each of these planets at 12:01 A.M., January 1, 1990 Earth time, at what Earth time would the next day begin on each planet?

Mercury	Venus	Mars	Jupiter

Saturn	Uranus	Neptune	Pluto

Monday

Unscramble each word. Which word names something that is not involved in photosynthesis?

banroc dixidoe   lugithns   ratew   ritvagy

Tuesday

If you lived on Jupiter, approximately how long would your summer vacation be, measured in Earth days?

Wednesday

Think of a sizzling hot barbeque grill. Can you give two examples of chemical changes in matter that may be taking place in it?

Thursday

Fill in the puzzle, using only words that identify types of body cells.

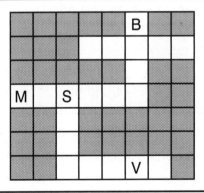

Friday

I am an imaginary line, but I can separate Tuesday from Wednesday. What is my name?

Weekly Challenge

In 1806, Sir Francis Beaufort created the Beaufort Wind Scale for sailing ships. Since then it has been adapted for use by meteorologists.

For each number on the scale of 0-12, there is given a weather term, a wind speed measured in miles per hour, and the typical effects of the wind on land.

Use the clues given in the table. Fill in the appropriate Beaufort number, the approximate wind speed, and the weather term.

	Clues	Beaufort Number, Wind Speed, Weather Term
1	As you walk out the door, you can feel the wind on your face.	#2 4–7 mph Light breeze
2	The smoke from the chimney next door is going straight up.	
3	As you turn the corner, you see roof tiles blowing off an apartment house.	
4	After the storm, you find that one of the trees on your street was uprooted.	
5	As you pass the pond, you notice white waves on it.	
6	When you return home after the storm, you find that many buildings have been devastated.	
7	Everything seems very still, but you notice that smoke from a chimney is drifting.	
8	As you look out the window, you notice that large branches are moving.	
9	When you leave home, you have some difficulty walking against the wind.	

Monday

Which of these statements is not always true?

1. Vertebrates have backbones.
2. Vertebrates stand up straight.
3. Vertebrates have a nervous system.
4. Vertebrates have a muscular system.

Tuesday

How long would it take sound to travel one mile on the moon?

Wednesday

Which of these materials are conductors of electricity?

plastic   ceramics   water   copper   glass

Thursday

Fill in the puzzle, using only words related to the parts of a flower.

Friday

I have one oxygen atom, but I am still poisonous. You cannot see me or smell me, but I am a form of pollution. What am I?

Weekly Challenge

Imagine that you are going to investigate the tidepools along a rocky coast of the Pacific Ocean. You will want to do some research on tides, because they affect what you will see in the tidepools. Find the answers to these questions.

1 How many tides are there in a day? What are their names?

2 When is the best time to visit the tidepool?

3 Where can you find out the times of the tides?

Now you are at the tidepool, and you have arrived at the best possible time. Record what plants and animals you could expect to see in each tidal zone. Also record any interesting facts about how the plants and animals in each zone interact with one another.

4 Spray zone, the highest part of the tidepool area

5 Upper-tide Zone, which is covered with water 2 to 3 hours

6 Mid-tide zone, which is uncovered only during low tides, 1 to 2 hours, 2 times a day

7 Low-tide zone, which is uncovered 1 to 3 hours, 2 times a month

THINK ABOUT IT! Science Problems of the Day

Monday

Give two examples of human parasites.

Tuesday

Fill in the puzzle, using only words related to the sun.

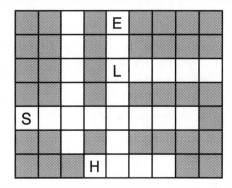

Wednesday

You want to magnify a butterfly so that you can see the colorful scales on its wings. Should you use a concave lens or a convex lens?

Thursday

It used to live in the southwestern United States. When it died, minerals replaced the wood fibers inside of it. What is it?

Friday

Three weeks after a New Moon, how much of the moon will be lighted?

Weekly Challenge

Make a list of all the simple machines you can locate on the bicycle and on the can opener.

Bicycle Part(s)	Simple Machine	Can Opener Part(s)	Simple Machine
wheels	wheel and axle		

THINK ABOUT IT! Science Problems of the Day   © 1993 Ideal School Supply Company

Monday

Tony is a long-distance runner. What type of food would be his best source of energy before an important race?

Tuesday

Name a mineral that has a Moh's rating of 7.

Wednesday

Name a percussion instrument that produces a low-pitched sound.

Thursday

Match each animal behavior with the name that tells what kind of behavior it is.
1. Bear hibernating
2. Seal balancing a ball
3. Mouse breathing
4. Chicken breaking out of shell
5. Worker ants providing food for a colony; soldier ants protecting the colony

a. Inborn behavior
b. Reflex
c. Instinct
d. Social behavior
e. Learned behavior

Friday

Natalie hopes to go someday to a continent that is nearly half the size of Africa, and a little over half the size of North America. There are no native human inhabitants on the continent. What continent does Natalie hope to visit?

Weekly Challenge

Different kinds of earth movements build different kinds of mountains.

Tell where these mountain ranges or systems are located in the U.S.A., and what kind of mountains they are as a result of the earth movements that helped build them.

	Mountain Range/ System	Location	Folded	Fault- Block	Domed	Volcanic
1	Sierra Nevadas	California		✔		
2	Black Hills	South Dakota, Wyoming				
3	Rocky Mountains					
4	Appalachians					
5	Cascades					
6	Wasatch Range					
7	Tetons					
8	Ozarks					

 THINK ABOUT IT! Science Problems of the Day

Monday

Unscramble each word. Which word names something that is not a consumer in a food chain?

neska   wakh   sumeo   deses

Tuesday

What takes the most time?

1. One revolution of the Earth
2. One revolution of the moon
3. One rotation of the Earth
4. One rotation of the moon

Wednesday

A certain instrument produces 75,000 vibrations per second. What animal or animals can hear that sound?

Thursday

Name two different invertebrates that you might find in a garden.

Friday

The molecules in one form of matter move more rapidly than in any other form of matter. Where would you find this form of matter?

Weekly Challenge

Animals can be grouped according to certain characteristics that they have in common.

Use the clues given in the table, and fill in the missing information.

	Animal Group	Vertebrate/ Invertebrate	Examples	Characteristics
1	Amphibians	V	salamander, frog	Need to keep skin moist. Live partly in water, partly on land.
2			oyster, octopus	
3				The most complex animals. Most are covered with hair.
4	Worms			Have segmented bodies. Many are parasites.
5	Sponges			Can regenerate missing parts. Water flows through their porous bodies.
6				Bodies covered by feathers. Warm-blooded.
7	Spiny-skinned	I		Have tube feet. These are the most complex invertebrates.
8	Fish		tiger shark, catfish	
9				Lay eggs on land. Have dry, scaly skin.
10	Arthropods		shrimp, centipede	

THINK ABOUT IT! Science Problems of the Day

Monday

What type of food does a bird usually eat if its beak is long and narrow?

Tuesday

Fill in the puzzle, using only words that identify forms of pollution.

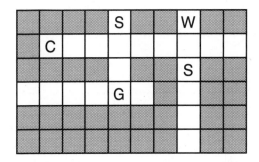

Wednesday

Which of these actions are examples of levers?

1. A batter hitting a baseball
2. A wheelbarrow carrying a load of bricks
3. A pair of scissors cutting a newspaper

Thursday

Animals often band together for different reasons. Name two different kinds of animals that band together, and tell why they do so.

Friday

Unscramble each word. Which words tell about what breaks down rocks through erosion?

hatreew   slatnp   tarwe   lisnama

Weekly Challenge

Each of the following sets of clues describes a particular kind of scientist. Use the clues to identify the scientist. Name the scientist and the tools he or she uses.

1 Many of the new celestial bodies I locate can't be seen with the naked eye. Unfortunately, I will never be able to visit many of the places I see from a distance.

Scientist: _____

Tools: _____

2 I am often covered with dust, while sifting for dead animals and plants in hot, dry places. All those jigsaw puzzles I put together as a kid have really helped me out on the job.

Scientist: _____

Tools: _____

3 My scuba-diving lessons have been very helpful in my work. I spend a lot of time on boats, as well as in the water. I study waves and currents and underwater mountains and valleys.

Scientist: _____

Tools: _____

4 The Latin that I learned has been very useful. I examine leaves and grasses wherever I go.

Scientist: _____

Tools: _____

5 I use my waders, especially when the streams are full and moving fast. I study fish in fresh water and salt water.

Scientist: _____

Tools: _____

6 I like to examine creatures that many people avoid. A lot of the creatures I handle are small and winged.

Scientist: _____

Tools: _____

7 I study the clouds, the wind, and air pressure.

Scientist: _____

Tools: _____

8 The hardness and appearance of rocks interest me. I like to examine the layers of soil around rocks.

Scientist: _____

Tools: _____

9 I study very small things, so small that I can't see them with my naked eye. I often examine single-cell organisms.

Scientist: _____

Tools: _____

10 The way plants and animals are dependent on each other and on their environments interests me.

Scientist: _____

Tools: _____

   THINK ABOUT IT! Science Problems of the Day   © 1993 Ideal School Supply Company

Monday

If an animal has very large cuspids and incisors, what kind of food does it probably eat?

Tuesday

What is the approximate distance from the bottom of the Mariana Trench to the top of Mount Everest?

Wednesday

June fills a balloon with 2 pints of water and places it in the freezer. How much does the balloon weigh 3 days later when she takes it out and weighs it?

Thursday

What are all the stages in the growth cycle of a frog?

Friday

What is the approximate difference in temperature between the hottest planet and the coldest planet, measured in degrees Celsius?

Weekly Challenge

Cyclones, hurricanes, and tornadoes are potentially dangerous weather conditions. Do some research and answer these questions about each condition:

a. Where is this condition most likely to occur?
b. At what time of year is it most likely to occur?
c. What would the temperature range be?
d. What would the range of wind speeds be?
e. What are some unique characteristics of this weather condition?
f. What is the worst occurrence of this weather condition in history that you can find?

1 Cyclone

a. _____
b. _____
c. _____
d. _____
e. _____
f. _____

2 Hurricane

a. _____
b. _____
c. _____
d. _____
e. _____
f. _____

3 Tornado

a. _____
b. _____
c. _____
d. _____
e. _____
f. _____

THINK ABOUT IT! Science Problems of the Day

Monday

Unscramble each word. Which word names something that an herbivore would eat?

grof   sifh   narig   morw   linas

Tuesday

Write a decimal that shows what part of air is oxygen.

Wednesday

What is another name for an inclined plane wrapped around a post?

Thursday

I am the only mammal that lays eggs. What am I?

Friday

The sailing crew has lost its way on the open seas. What celestial body will help them find their way home?

Weekly Challenge

An ecosystem is a community of particular plants and animals that interact with one another in order to survive.

Each set of clues below gives characteristics of plants belonging to a particular ecosystem. Identify the ecosystem in which those plants live.

1 The trees are deciduous, and the leaves change color. Some seeds are formed in cones.

   Ecosystem: _____

2 The plants have wide-spreading roots, spiny leaves, and their surfaces are waxy.

   Ecosystem: _____

3 Some plants are growing on other plants. Some plants have no roots. There are many bright, colorful flowers.

   Ecosystem: _____

4 The plants have broad leaves and are rooted underwater. There is rapid growth of plants here.

   Ecosystem: _____

5 Plant growth is sparse with tall, slender stems and shallow root systems. Seeds usually are spiny or sticky, and most of them are transported by wind or animals.

   Ecosystem: _____

6 The plant life is short, abundant, and close to the ground. Grasses predominate, and flowers are in ample supply.

   Ecosystem: _____

Monday

Betty is examining platelets. What instrument is she using?

Tuesday

If you could dig a hole 592 kilometers deep, what layer of the Earth would you reach?

Wednesday

What is the mass of one liter of H_2O on the moon?

Thursday

I have the longest gestation period of any mammal. What am I?

Friday

What does this show?

Sun

Earth

Moon

Weekly Challenge

What are some of the best sources from which your body can get its supply of the vitamins and minerals shown below? For what does your body use the vitamins and minerals?

	Vitamin/ Mineral	Best Sources	Use In Your Body
1	vitamin A	green leafy vegetables, broccoli, carrots, apricots, mangoes, milk	for growth and repair of body tissues; for maintaining good eyesight
2	vitamin B$_1$		
3	vitamin B$_2$		
4	vitamin B$_6$		
5	vitamin B$_{12}$		
6	vitamin C		
7	vitamin D		
8	vitamin E		
9	vitamin K		
10	calcium		
11	iron		
12	fluorine		
13	phosphorus		
14	potassium		
15	sodium		

THINK ABOUT IT! Science Problems of the Day

Monday

All living things contain at least one of me. Sometimes I am alone; but most times I work with others just like me. I can take in food, grow, and reproduce. I am basic to all life. What am I?

Tuesday

In which of the following conditions will water evaporate fastest?

1. 86° F, 95% humidity, wind speeds at 2 knots
2. 31° C, 51% humidity, wind speeds at 10 mph
3. 10° C, 89% humidity, wind speeds at 17 knots

Wednesday

Unscramble each word. Which word names something that is not an example of a simple machine?

finek   norbodok   esewas   doari

Thursday

Can you think of three ways in which whales and gorillas are similar?

Three ways in which they are different?

Friday

Weathering has changed rocks into their smallest form in the area where Eric lives. Where does he live?

Weekly Challenge

You won't find a tarantula and an egret in the same area, unless perhaps in a zoo! This is because they live in different ecosystems. An ecosystem is a community of particular plants and animals that interact with one another in order to survive.

Identify the ecosystem where you would find each of the following groups of plants and animals. Identify the name of the plant or animal that does NOT belong in each group.

1   Pine tree, blue jay, squirrel, bees, earthworm, poison oak, gila monster, fir

     Ecosystem: _____

     What doesn't belong? _____

2   Cholla, hawk, rattlesnake, lizard, ivy, saguaro, rabbit, tumbleweed

     Ecosystem: _____

     What doesn't belong? _____

3   Turtle, dragonfly, alligator, sequoia, spider, cattails, water snake, perch

     Ecosystem: _____

     What doesn't belong? _____

4   Pelican, seal, otter, seagull, clam, fly, marmot

     Ecosystem: _____

     What doesn't belong? _____

5   Mouse, heron, pickleweed, egret, shrimp, oak tree

     Ecosystem: _____

     What doesn't belong? _____

    THINK ABOUT IT! Science Problems of the Day   © 1993 Ideal School Supply Company

Monday

What is missing from this food chain?

humans $\longrightarrow$ tuna $\longrightarrow$ $\longrightarrow$ plant plankton

Tuesday

Gene sets off on a raft at Seattle, Washington. If his raft drifts freely for 1700 miles in the Pacific Ocean, where will he end up? (Hint: In what direction will the ocean current carry him?)

Wednesday

Unscramble each word. Which word is another name for iron oxide?

sutr   letse   goynex   tonegrin

Thursday

Name two extinct species of animals.

Name two endangered species of animals.

Friday

What are Io, Ganymede, and Amalthea?

Weekly Challenge

Imagine that you were visiting a friend when an earthquake occurred. When it was all over, you found out that the quake measured 8.6 on the Richter Scale. Think about the possible answers to these questions, and then record your answers.

1 What are some possible places that you could have been visiting?

2 What kinds of warnings might there have been that the earthquake would occur?

    a. What warnings might you have noticed?

    b. What warnings would you not have noticed?

3 What is the Richter Scale? What does it mean that the earthquake measured 8.6 on the scale?

4 What did you feel and notice during the earthquake?

5 What happened after the earthquake, something that you could feel?

6 What did you see after the earthquake?

Monday

Which one of these items does not belong in any of the four food groups?

apples   rice   beef   cauliflower   cheese   sugar   turkey

Tuesday

Unscramble each word. Which planet was farthest from the sun during the bicentennial of the U.S. Constitution?

rantus   sarnuu   loput   tennepu

Wednesday

Which would cover the longer distance: light traveling for 3 seconds, or sound traveling for 100 seconds?

Thursday

How many ovaries does a conifer have?

Friday

Emily goes aloft in a hot-air balloon at Omaha, Nebraska. If she travels exactly 500 miles, which state will she probably land in? (*Hint:* In what direction will the prevailing winds take her?)

Weekly Challenge

How much energy does it take to make vanilla ice cream? A lot more than you might expect!

Here is a recipe for making ice cream. For each ingredient, record the source, the type of energy needed to produce the source, and whether that energy is renewable. Then record the type of energy needed to manufacture or prepare the ingredient for market, and whether the energy is renewable.

Vanilla Ice Cream

$\frac{2}{3}$ cup sugar
$1\frac{1}{2}$ cups milk
2 eggs
$2\frac{1}{2}$ tsp vanilla
$\frac{1}{4}$ tsp salt
1 cup cream
$1\frac{1}{2}$ tbsp cornstarch

Ingredient	Source	Energy to Produce Source	Renewable?	Energy to Manufacture Source	Renewable?
sugar	sugar cane	sun	yes	mechanical & electrical	no
milk					
eggs					
vanilla					
salt					
cream					
cornstarch					

THINK ABOUT IT! *Science Problems of the Day*

Monday

Why do kidneys, lungs, and skin belong in the same class?

Tuesday

If you lived in New Zealand, during what day of the year would the sun's rays be most direct?

Wednesday

Marcia has difficulty seeing objects that are far away from her. What shape should the lenses in her eyeglasses be?

Thursday

Unscramble each word. Which word names something that would be listed second in a diagram of a food chain?

knotapnl   gennupi   lirlk   leas

Friday

Venus and Uranus do something no other planets do. What is it?

Weekly Challenge

Can you name these mystery compounds?

1 I am made up of oxygen and iron.
My chemical symbol is FeO_2.

What am I? _____

2 I am made up of carbon and oxygen.
My chemical symbol is CO.

What am I? _____

3 I am made up of sodium and chloride.
My chemical symbol is NaCl.

What am I? _____

4 I am made up of carbon and oxygen.
My chemical symbol is CO_2.

What am I? _____

5 I am made up of carbon, hydrogen, and oxygen.
My chemical symbol is $C_6H_{12}O_6$.

What am I? _____

6 I am made up of hydrogen and chloride.
My chemical symbol is HCl.

What am I? _____

7 I am made up of hydrogen and oxygen.
My chemical symbol is H_2O.

What am I? _____

8 I am made up of sulfur and oxygen.
My chemical symbol is SO_2.

What am I? _____

THINK ABOUT IT! Science Problems of the Day   © 1993 Ideal School Supply Company

Monday

Unscramble each word. Which words name evergreen trees?

nepi   cebhe   repscu   rif   lamep

Tuesday

Henry lives in a city that has air pressure of about 15 pounds per square inch. Which of these cities does he not live in?

Los Angeles   Denver   New York   Chicago

Wednesday

Name two woodwind instruments that produce slow vibrations.

Thursday

Name a plant that produces a crop used in the manufacture of clothing.

Friday

Brenda's birthday in December is on the one day of the year that has the longest period of daylight. What hemisphere does she live in?

Weekly Challenge

Tidal waves, flash floods, and avalanches all involve rapid movement of water in liquid or solid form. Do some research and answer these questions about each natural event:

    a. Where is this event most likely to occur?
    b. At what time of year is it most likely to happen?
    c. What other kind of event might this one follow?
    d. What are some unique characteristics of this natural occurrence?

1   Tidal wave

    a. _____

    b. _____

    c. _____

    d. _____

2   Flash flood

    a. _____

    b. _____

    c. _____

    d. _____

3   Avalanche

    a. _____

    b. _____

    c. _____

    d. _____

Monday

Unscramble each word. Which words name creatures that live in an intertidal zone?

timleps   egala   larco   yhljfseli   darbacura

Tuesday

Fill in the puzzle, using only words that identify agents of erosion.

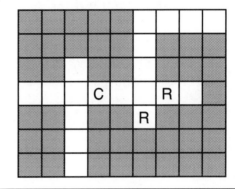

Wednesday

What does a galvanometer measure?

Thursday

What kind of instrument would you use to view an amoeba?

telescope   microscope   stethoscope

Friday

In what way are Cassiopeia, Orion, and Canis Major alike?

Weekly Challenge

Observing the temperature, seasons, sources of food and water, and other factors about an environment can often help you predict what kinds of animals and plants will live in that ecological community.

Read the description of each environment. Then create an imaginary plant and an imaginary animal that could survive in that environment. Describe or draw the plant and the animal.

1   The ground is covered with snow year-round, and the temperature seldom rises above 32°F.

2   The temperature is constantly above 100°F. There is very little water in this flat, sandy area.

3   There is a lot of silt and mud in these very warm, constantly changing waters.

4   Temperature varies widely here. There is a good deal of rainfall and high winds.

THINK ABOUT IT! Science Problems of the Day   © 1993 Ideal School Supply Company

Monday

What kind of doctor would perform surgery on a person's left ventricle?

Tuesday

It is 36°C in Santiago, Chile. Which way is the Earth tilted on its axis?

Wednesday

Steffen dropped ice cubes into a pan and put the pan on a hot burner. By the time the water began to boil, how many small calories of heat energy had been absorbed by each gram of water in the pan?

Thursday

What does a botanist study?

Friday

A Dingo dog is watching water swirl down a bathtub drain in a clockwise motion. What country is the dog in?

Weekly Challenge

Volcanoes have fascinated people for centuries. They build, but they also destroy.

Answer the following questions about volcanoes. Use resources such as encyclopedias and almanacs if you need information.

1   Where are there volcanoes in the United States, and are they active or inactive?

2   Where and when was there a recent eruption of a volcano in the United States?

    a. Describe what happened during the eruption.

    b. What was the effect of the eruption on the people, plants, and animals living near the volcano?

    c. What is it like now in the area around the volcano?

3   Where are there some volcanoes outside of the United States?

4   Where and when was the famous eruption of Mount Vesuvius?

    What happened to the city of Pompeii as a result of that eruption?

Monday

Craig notices that the respiration rate of plants decreases during a certain time of the year. What season could this be?

Tuesday

What is the "Ring of Fire"? Why is it important to geologists?

Wednesday

You watch a bolt of lightning streak through the air from one cloud to another. Three seconds later you hear thunder. How many yards away from you are the two clouds?

Thursday

A bird stands up and looks around. Every direction it looks is north. What animal could it be, and where is it?

Friday

What atmospheric conditions contribute to the highest rate of transpiration?

Weekly Challenge

When you compare Earth with Venus, Mars, and Jupiter, you find that there are some interesting similarities and differences.

1   The force of gravity is much stronger on Jupiter than on Earth, but less strong on Mars than on Earth. How much do you weigh on Earth? _____ How much would you weigh on Jupiter? _____ How much would you weigh on Mars? _____

2   Approximately how many pounds of atmospheric pressure are there per square inch on Earth? _____ How many times greater is the atmospheric pressure on Venus than on Earth? _____ Approximately how many pounds of pressure are there per square inch on Venus? _____

How much less is the atmospheric pressure on Mars than on Earth? _____ Approximately how many pounds of pressure are there per square inch on Mars? _____

3   Which planets have lightning? _____

4   Which planets have volcanoes and canyons? _____

5   Which planets have craters? _____

6   Which planets have rocks on their surfaces? _____

7   Which planet does not appear to have a solid crust? _____

8   Which planet has a 13,000-mile-wide storm raging all the time? _____ What is the storm called? _____

Monday

What kind of an environment do bacteria need for reproducing and multiplying?

Tuesday

When does a comet's tail travel in front of the comet rather than behind it?

Wednesday

Unscramble each word. Which words name things that are examples of potential energy?

odow   niprgs   nus   loca   losnaige

Thursday

Fill in the puzzle, using only words that identify classes of vertebrates.

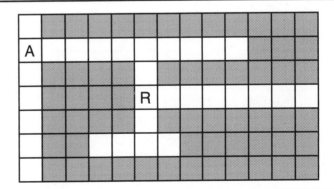

Friday

Which hemisphere contains most of the world's oceans?

Weekly Challenge

Shown below are partial weather reports from various cities in the United States. Read each one and try to identify a major U.S. city that would have that weather. (There may be more than one city that would have that weather.)

1 "Air quality was poor today as a high pressure system hovered off the coast, holding in the smog and high temperatures."

City: _____

2 "Temperatures were again over 100 degrees today. Dry, dusty winds from the southwest continue to blow. The relative humidity will be in the low 20s."

City: _____

3 "Last night's blizzard left over 22 inches of new snow on the ground, and southwesterly winds promise another dumping tonight in this mile-high city."

City: _____

4 "A fifth straight day of precipitation. Westerly winds look like they'll be bringing in lots of moisture from the ocean again. In other words, it's weather as usual."

City: _____

5 "Wild, blustery winds off the lake today played havoc during rush hour. Snow from last night's blizzard has blown into piles over 10 feet high on many roads."

City: _____

6 "People headed for tonight's game at The Garden should take extra time and care. Most roads have been plowed, but secondary roads are covered with ice."

City: _____

7 "The city is covered by a dense fog. A light breeze is blowing from the south, with temperatures in the 50s."

City: _____

8 "High humidity, with temperatures in the 80s. No wind is expected off the ocean today."

City: _____

9 "Tornado warnings are in effect this afternoon and evening, as a string of thunderheads sweeps up from the south. A week of high humidity is being blamed."

City: _____

THINK ABOUT IT! Science Problems of the Day

Solution Key

Page 1

M	Statement 3
Tu	Oil, wood, <u>gas</u>, <u>coal</u>
W	Gravity
Th	

```
            D E N S
          L       E
          C A V E S
          I       T
      B U R R O W S
          S
```

F	Stalagmite

Page 2

2	Whale, calf, bull
3	Cub, she-bear/sow, boar, sleuth
4	Chicken, rooster, brood/clutch, coop
5	Horse, mare, stallion, pasture/farm
6	Tiger, cub, tiger, pack, lair
7	Cub, lioness, lion, pride
8	Hare, buck, down/husk, burrow/hutch
9	Chick, hen, cock, bevy/covey, tall grasses
10	Pig, sow, boar, litter

Page 3

M	Skin
Tu	The same amount of air pressure was on all of them.
W	800 grams
Th	Nerves
F	The moon

Page 4

1	Fireflies
2	Processionary caterpillars
3	Rhinoceros beetle, Southeast Asia
4	Atlas moth, wingspan of 12 inches
5	Leaf-cutter bee, from Malay Archipelago, 1 ½ inches long
6	Goliath beetle, from Africa
7	It gives birth to live babies most of the year. Ants keep a "herd" of greenflies for their milk, like a dairy farmer keeps cows.
8	It can move in any direction while in flight, even backwards.
9	Ephemeral fly
10	Black widow spider

Page 5

M	Salmon or eel
Tu	7; 2
W	Air/oxygen/gas
Th	Pecan, <u>peanut</u>, walnut, cashew
F	A volcano

Page 6

Vertical symmetry: A H I M O T U V W X Y
Horizontal symmetry: B C D E H I O X
Both: H I O X
Neither: G J K L N P Q R S Z (N, S, and Z have radial symmetry, but not line symmetry.)

The human, dog, bird, frog, and spider have vertical symmetry; the clam has horizontal symmetry; and the amoeba has neither vertical nor horizontal symmetry.

Page 7

M	Male seahorse
Tu	Coral reef
W	Black; no
Th	<u>Beaver</u>, <u>dolphin</u>, <u>raccoon</u>, snail
F	Mercury

Page 8

1	The snowshoe hare and the arctic fox have brown fur in summer and white fur in winter, to match their surroundings.
2	The king snake mimics the coral snake, which is dangerous.
3	The sphinx moth has bright colors on its wings to scare away birds.
4	The monarch butterfly has bright colors, which protects it from predators.
5	The leaf butterfly looks like a small leaf, so it blends into its surroundings.
6	The ptarmigan is white in one season, brown in another. Its colors match its surroundings.
7	The katydid has wings that look exactly like green leaves.
8	The walking stick resembles a stick.
9	The stingray cannot be seen from above; it uses color to hide itself.
10	The robber fly mimics the colors of a bumblebee.

Page 9

M	Seaweed or kelp
Tu	<u>meteor</u>, star, comet, asteroid
W	28 mi/h
Th	Herbivore: cow, deer, rabbit, giraffe, caterpillar; carnivore: tiger, hawk, shark, seal, owl; omnivore: bear, rat, raccoon, turtle
F	Light

Page 10

1) Mirror; 2) shiny side of foil, smooth; 3) shiny side of foil, wrinkled; 4) glass object; 5) white paper, smooth; 6) white paper, wrinkled; 7) dull side of foil, smooth; 8) dull side of foil, wrinkled; 9) white shirt; 10) yellow paper; 11) black paper

Page 11

M	<u>Turtle</u>, <u>snake</u>, frog, <u>lizard</u>, <u>crocodile</u>
Tu	A warm front moving east
W	Friction
Th	Mushroom
F	21 pounds

Page 12

2	Muscles, ligaments, tendons
3	Excretory; lungs, skin, large intestine
4	Skeletal; skull, spinal column, ribs, bones in limbs
5	Nervous; brain, spinal cord
6	Digestive; prepares food for use by body
7	Pituitary gland, thyroid glands, adrenal glands; growth, metabolism, blood sugar
8	Respiratory; brings oxygen to body parts

Page 13

M

		R		C				
	P	E		O				
	U	T		R		I		L
O	P	T	I	C	-	N	E	R	V	E
	I	N		E		I		N
	L	A		A		S		S

Tu	Lava
W	They were slowing down.
Th	22 inches
F	A flat-topped, underwater mountain

Page 14

2	Sedimentary
3	Quartzite; metamorphic
4	Igneous; slowly cooling magma, then great pressure
5	Sugary appearance, grainy; sediments of sand cemented over time
6	Pumice
7	Hardest mineral, cannot be scratched by other minerals; great pressure over long periods of time
8	Marble; great heat and pressure
9	Used as chalk
10	Obsidian; igneous

Page 15

M	Land: buffalo, caribou; water: whale, salmon, trout; air: Arctic tern, swallows, monarch butterflies
Tu	Pacific Ocean
W	Element, <u>compound</u>, atom, molecule
Th	The pitcher plant has tube-like leaves with downward-pointing hairs to prevent insects from crawling back out. The Venus's-flytrap has teeth or hairs on its leaves, and it secretes a sticky liquid. The sundew has tentacle-like hairs on its leaves, and the tips of the hairs have glands which secrete a sticky fluid that glistens like dew. The butterwort has a sticky fluid on the surface of its leaves. The bladderwort has a sac with a door at one end; the door closes, a vacuum is created in the sac, and when prey touch bristles on the door, the door opens and the prey is drawn into the sac by the vacuum.
F	Philippines

Page 16

1	On their legs — locusts; on the sides of their body — moths; on the sides of their head — mammals; on their antennae — mosquitos
2	Fish — hairs, skin organs; frogs — hairs
3	Ultrasonic — bats, whales, dogs; subsonic — seals, walruses
4	Echo location — bats, whales, porpoises, dolphins; sonar — whales, dolphins

Page 17

M	Skeleton

Tu

							O		H
	C	A	L	I	F	O	R	N	I	A
							E		W
							G		A
W	A	S	H	I	N	G	T	O	N		I
							N		I

W	Water
Th	<u>Water</u>, <u>insects</u>, <u>wind</u>, <u>birds</u>, sun
F	Water

Page 18

1 Yes, no, no, yes
2 Yes, no, no, yes
3 No, no, yes, no
4 Yes, yes, yes, no
5 No, yes, yes, no
6 Yes, no, no, no
7 Yes, no, no, yes
8 No, yes, yes, no
9 Yes, no, yes or no, no
10 No, yes, yes, no

Riding a roller coaster, operating an electric train or slot cars, running a vacuum cleaner, and using an electromagnet at a junkyard would each involve all four forces.

Page 19

M   The anvil, stirrup, and hammer transmit sound energy to the inner ear.
Tu Troposhere
W   Diamond
Th Lettuce, rice, cereal, bread, potato
F   Seismograph

Page 20 (samples)

Category 2: Animals without fur: toad, turtle, butterfly, trout, vulture

Category 3: Animals that are carnivorous: kangaroo, toad, turtle, vulture, bear, trout

Category 4: Animals that are predators: trout, toad, vulture, bear, turtle (some eat insects)

Category 5: Animals that are mammals: kangaroo, porcupine, rabbit, elephant, bear

Page 21

M   200
Tu Jenny
W   The root
Th Stem, root, stalk, leaves
F   4

Page 22

1 Arctic Ocean
2 Pacific Ocean
3 Caribbean Sea
4 Red Sea
5 Indian Ocean
6 Antarctic Ocean
7 Atlantic Ocean
8 Gulf of Mexico
9 Mediterranean Sea

Page 23

M   Beets, turnips, carrots
Tu

W   Scale
Th Oxygen
F   Glacier

Page 24

2   Conserve water
3   Use heat; use electricity
4   Conserve fossil fuels
5   Use electricity; conserve fossil fuels
6   Conserve heat, electricity, fossil fuels
7   Use electricity
8   Conserve heat, electricity, fossil fuels
9   Conserve heat, water, electricity, fossil fuels
10 Conserve heat, electricity, fossil fuels

Page 25

M   Eggs, milk, butter; vitamin D is needed for healthy bones and teeth.
Tu 3
W

Th 6
F   1986

Page 26

1   **Predators:** snake, mouse, lizard, woodpecker
    Prey: fly, grubs, rodents, beetle
2   **Predators:** owl, hawk, bear, wolf, bobcat, weasel, anteater, lion
    Prey: mouse, rabbit, ants, deer, rat, salmon, hare, antelope
3   **Predators:** shark, pelican, bass, trout
    Prey: perch, minnows, frog, nymph
4   **Predators:** spider, tern, heron, crab, duck, hawk
    Prey: clam, crab, minnow, moth, grasshopper

Page 27

M   Protein, vitamins, minerals
Tu Asteroid, universe, galaxy, solar system
W   Bernie
Th Potato
F   Fair weather

Page 28

2   Auriga
3   King
4   Orion; Mighty Hunter
5   Ursa Minor; Little Dipper
6   Orion's Dog; Sirius; winter
7   Queen; none; all seasons
8   Scorpion; summer
9   Regulus; spring

Page 29

M   Oranges, lemons, limes, grapefruit; vitamin C is needed for healthy gums, bones, connective tissue, and capillaries.
Tu Desert, prairie, steppe, veldt
W

Th Moth, butterfly, locust, frog, toad
F   6 minutes 40 seconds (approximately)

Page 30

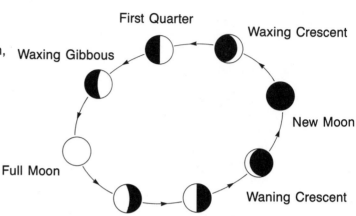

First Quarter
Waxing Crescent
Waxing Gibbous
New Moon
Full Moon
Waning Crescent
Waning Gibbous
Last Quarter

Page 31

M   Warmth, air, soil, water, fertilizer
Tu

	H		S	L	E	E	T
R	A	I	N				
	I		O				
	L		W				

W

Th Lungfish
F   1/2000 of a ton of coffee on Earth

Page 32

2   Rabbit, because hawks don't eat rabbits.
3   Turtle, because bears don't eat turtles.
4   Deer, because deer don't feed on snakes.
5   Dolphin, because dolphins don't eat tuna.
6   Butterfly, because butterflies don't consume grasshoppers.
7   Weasel, because weasels don't eat rattlesnakes.
8   Coyote, because coyotes don't eat hawks.
9   Deer, because deer don't eat trout.

Page 33

M

		R		L	
F	L	O	W	E	R
		O		A	
		T		V	
		S	T	E	M
				S	

Tu Statement 3
W   3,710 feet
Th Leaf, petal, stamen, ovule, pistil
F   Low tide

Page 34

2 Strings; high and low; fast and slow
3 Beating on animal skin; low; slow
4 Vocal cords; low; slow
5 Reed; high; fast
6 Strings; high; fast
7 Column of air; high; fast
8 Column of air; high; fast
9 Reed; high; fast
10 Strings; low; slow
11 Strings; low; slow
12 Sticks hitting metal bars; high and low; fast and slow

Page 35

M Anything made with sugar
Tu Saturn, Venus, Neptune, Jupiter
W 4 seconds
Th Two chemicals: luciferin and luciferase
F Anemometer

Page 36

1 Mercury 36,000,000; Venus 67,000,000; Earth 93,000,000; Mars 141,000,000; Jupiter 480,000,000

2 Answers will vary. Average temperatures on the named planets are: Mercury 770°F; Venus 752°F; Neptune 392°F; Saturn −290°F; Uranus −328°F; Mars −11°F

3 Mercury 12:01 A.M., June 25, 1990
Venus 2:25 P.M., April 26, 1990
Mars 12:37 A.M., January 2, 1990
Jupiter 9:55 A.M., January 1, 1990
Saturn 10:25 A.M., January 1, 1990
Uranus 4:01 P.M., January 1, 1990
Neptune 6:31 P.M., January 1, 1990
Pluto 6:01 A.M., January 7, 1990

Page 37

M Carbon dioxide, sunlight, water, gravity
Tu 1095 days, or 3 years
W Burning wood or charcoal, and rusting metal
Th

				B		
		B	L	O	O	D
				N		
M	U	S	C	L	E	
		K				
		I				
		N	E	R	V	E

F International date line

Page 38

1 #2; 4–7 mph; Light breeze
2 #0; less than 1 mph; Calm
3 #9; 47–54 mph; Strong gale
4 #10; 55–63 mph; Whole gale
5 #5; 19–24 mph; Fresh breeze
6 #12; 73+ mph; Hurricane
7 #1; 1–3 mph; Light air
8 #6; 25–31 mph; Strong breeze
9 #8; 39–46 mph; Fresh gale

Page 39

M Statement 2
Tu Sound cannot travel on the moon.
W Water, copper
Th

		S				O	
P	I	S	T	I	L		V
		A					A
		M					R
		E	M	B	R	Y	O
		N					

F Carbon monoxide

Page 40

1. 4 tides; 2 high tides, 2 low tides
2. During a minus tide, when the low-tide zone can be seen
3. From tide tables in a newspaper or in a sporting goods store
4. Sea moss, limpets, barnacles, snails (periwinkle), rock louse (sow bug)
5. Worms, hermit crabs, rock snail, anemones, lined shore crab, barnacles, black turban snail, limpets, brown rockweeds, sea sac, Old Man's Beard
6. Sea lettuce, rockweed, algae, volcano limpets, goose barnacle, link confetti, purple snails, brown turban snails, mussels, brittle star, limpet, chiton, sea anemones, abalone, kelp crab, starfish
7. Brown kelp, red rock crust, eel grass, surf grass, sea palm, starfish, kelp crab, sea urchins, abalone, nudibranch, octopuses, mussels, boring clams, sea cucumbers, limpets, chitons, sponges

Page 41

M Tapeworm, bacterium, fungus

Tu

W Convex lens
Th Petrified wood
F One half

Page 42

Bicycle Parts	Simple Machine
wheels	wheel and axle
derailer	wheel and axle
front sprocket	wheel and axle
gear wheels	pulley
pedals	wheel and axle
handlebars	wheel and axle
brake handles	lever

Can Opener Parts	Simple Machine
handles	lever
turning key	wheel and axle
cutting blade	inclined plane

Page 43

M Carbohydrates
Tu Quartz
W Bass drum
Th 1—c, 2—e, 3—b, 4—a, 5—d
F Antarctica

Page 44

2. South Dakota, Wyoming; domed
3. Alaska, Montana, Wyoming, Colorado, New Mexico, Texas; folded, fault-block, and volcanic
4. Alabama, Tennessee, North Carolina, Virginia, Maryland, Pennsylvania, New York, Vermont, New Hampshire, Maine; folded
5. California, Oregon, Washington; volcanic
6. Utah, Idaho; fault-block
7. Wyoming; fault-block
8. Missouri, Arkansas, Oklahoma; domed

Page 45

M Snake, hawk, mouse, seeds
Tu Statement 1
W Bat, porpoise
Th Snail, slug, earthworm
F In the atmosphere

Page 46

2. Mollusks; invertebrate
   Often called shellfish. Some have shells, but not all.
3. Mammals; vertebrate; dolphin, monkey
4. Invertebrate; roundworm, tapeworm
5. Invertebrate; sponge
6. Birds; vertebrate; ostrich, eagle
7. Starfish, sea urchin
8. Vertebrates
   They take oxygen from the water. It is the simplest group of vertebrates.
9. Reptiles; vertebrate; crocodile, gila monster
10. Invertebrate
    They have segmented bodies, outer skeletons, and jointed legs.

Page 47

M   Insects

Tu

				S			W		
	C	H	E	M	I	C	A	L	S
				O			S		
S	E	W	A	G	E		T		
							E		
							S		

W   All three

Th   Deer and elk band together for protection; wolves and coyotes often band together to hunt for food; honeybees band together and divide up the work.

F   <u>Weather</u>, plants, <u>water</u>, animals

Page 48

1. Astronomer; telescope, sky map
2. Paleontologist; shovel, pick, microscope
3. Oceanographer; sonar, bathyscaphe
4. Botanist; microscope
5. Ichthyologist; knife, microscope
6. Entomologist; tweezers, microscope
7. Meteorologist; barometer, anemometer, thermometer
8. Geologist; pick, shovel, map
9. Microbiologist; microscope
10. Ecologist; maps, charts, field glasses

Page 49

M   Meat
Tu   20,000 meters or 65,000 feet
W   2.08 pounds (approximately)
Th   Egg, embryo, larva, tadpole, adult frog
F   680°C

Page 50

1. Cyclone
   a. India; Tropics
   b. Late spring, summer
   c. Warm, moist air
   d. 200–300 mph
   e. Rapidly spinning air mass; counterclockwise in N. Hemisphere, clockwise in S. Hemisphere
   f. November 13–14, 1970; Bangladesh; more than 1,000,000 people died

2. Hurricane
   a. Develops over ocean
   b. Late summer; early fall
   c. Warm, moist air
   d. 73–136 mph
   e. Rotating mass of air; affects large area
   f. Hurricane Camille; 1969; more than 250 people died

3. Tornado
   a. Midwest; south central states
   b. Late spring; early summer
   c. Cold air layer over warm air mass
   d. Up to 300 mph
   e. Great contrast between polar and tropical air masses
   f. April 3–4, 1974; Alabama, Ohio, Kentucky, Georgia, Tennessee; more than 300 people died

Page 51

M   Frog, fish, <u>grain</u>, worm, snail
Tu   0.21
W   Screw
Th   Duckbill platypus
F   North Star

Page 52

1. Forest
2. Desert
3. Tropical rain forest
4. Fresh-water pond
5. Chaparral
6. Meadow

Page 53

M   Microscope
Tu   Mantle
W   1 kilogram
Th   African elephant
F   Eclipse of the moon

Page 54

2   bran, wheat germ, sunflower seeds, nuts, pork, beans; for supplying energy and for maintenance of the nervous system, heart, liver

3   liver, whole milk, yogurt, almonds, wheat germ, mushrooms, turnip greens; for supplying energy and for maintaining healthy eyes

4   whole grains, meats, nuts; for metabolism and the maintenance of the central nervous system

5   meats, fish, milk, eggs, soybeans; for keeping all cells healthy, especially bone marrow, gastrointestinal tract, nerve tissue, red blood cells

6   broccoli, Brussels sprouts, persimmons, strawberries, citrus fruits, parsley; for maintaining healthy skin, gums, ligaments, bones, and for healing wounds

7   sunlight, fatty fish, fish liver oil, egg yolk, milk products; for maintaining healthy bones and for regulating calcium and phosphorus in the blood

8   wheat germ, fruits, peanuts, eggs, green leafy vegetables, vegetable oils; for protecting red blood cells and for healing burns, bruises, wounds

9   green leafy vegetables, alfalfa sprouts, fats, oats, wheat, rye; for blood-clotting

10   sesame seeds, cheese, kelp, dairy products, kale, turnip and collard greens, almonds, molasses; for building and maintaining teeth and bones, and for regulating pH balance in blood

11   liver, shellfish, molasses, beans, green leafy vegetables, egg yolk; for helping build materials in the blood which transport oxygen to muscles

12   seafood, fluorinated water, flouride toothpaste, vegetables; for building and maintaining strong teeth and bones

13   wheat germ, fish, chicken, meats, seeds, legumes, dairy products; for building and repairing cells and for supplying energy for muscle contraction and nerve impulses

14   legumes, green leafy vegetables, grains, nuts, fruits, seafood, root vegetables; for regulating the pH balance in the blood and for affecting muscle activity

15   table salt, green leafy vegetables, dairy products; for regulating the pH balance in the blood and for affecting muscle activity

Page 55

M   Cell

Tu   Condition 2

W   Knife, doorknob, seesaw, radio

Th   Similarities—both mammals, breathe oxygen, bear live young, and are large animals. Differences—whales live in water, gorillas on land; whales eat plankton, gorillas eat fruits and vegetables; whales have no necks, gorillas have necks; gorillas have hairy covering, whales have no hair or few hairs on skin.

F   Sandy area, probably near shore of body of water

Page 56

1   Forest; gila monster
2   Desert; ivy
3   Swamplands; sequoia
4   Seashore; marmot
5   Baylands/marshlands; oak tree

Page 57

M   Shrimp or small fish
Tu   Mexico
W   Rust, steel, oxygen, nitrogen
Th   Extinct—dodo, dinosaur, moa, passenger pigeon, great auk; endangered—bald eagle, whooping crane
F   Moons of Jupiter

Page 58

1   California, Alaska (if in U.S.A.)
2   a. Tremors of the earth, and unusual animal behavior
     b. Plate slippage along a fault line
3   The Richter Scale measures the strength of earthquakes; 8.6 means the quake was very powerful
4   Earth moving, buckling, shaking, vibrating; buildings collapsing; cracks in street
5   Aftershocks
6   Damaged buildings; severe cracks in earth; destruction; loss of electricity

Page 59

M   Sugar
Tu   Saturn, Uranus, Pluto, Neptune
W   Light traveling for 3 seconds
Th   None
F   Indiana

Page 60

2 **milk:** cow (grass); sun; yes; heat and electrical; no
3 **eggs:** chicken (feed); sun; yes
4 **vanilla:** vanilla bean; sun; yes; chemical, mechanical, and electrical; no
5 **salt:** salt water and salt deposits; heat; yes; chemical and heat; no
6 **cream:** cow (grass); sun; yes; mechanical and electrical; no
7 **cornstarch:** corn; sun; yes; mechanical and electrical; no

Page 61

M They are all part of the excretory system.
Tu December 21 or 22
W Concave
Th Plankton, penguin, <u>krill</u>, seal
F Rotate east to west

Page 62

1 Rust
2 Carbon monoxide
3 Salt
4 Carbon dioxide
5 Sugar
6 Hydrochloric acid
7 Water
8 Sulfuric acid

Page 63

M <u>Pine</u>, beech, <u>spruce</u>, <u>fir</u>, maple
Tu Denver
W Bassoon, English horn, clarinet
Th Cotton
F Southern Hemisphere

Page 64

1 Tidal wave
  a. Along the seashore (Hawaii, Alaska, West Coast)
  b. Any time
  c. Earthquake, hurricane
  d. Large waves which move great distances over an ocean

2 Flash flood
  a. Dry river beds (Southwest)
  b. Spring, early summer
  c. Severe rains
  d. Cause severe property damage; often unpredictable

3 Avalanche
  a. Mountains, ski areas (Colorado, Rockies)
  b. Winter
  c. Heavy snowfall
  d. Large mass of snow, travels rapidly; destructive

Page 65

M <u>Limpets</u>, <u>algae</u>, <u>coral</u>, <u>jellyfish</u>, barracuda

Tu

					W	I	N	D
					A			
		W			T			
G	L	A	C	I	E	R	S	
		V			R			
		E						
		S						

W Current electricity
Th Microscope
F They are all constellations.

Page 66

These are the general characteristics needed by the plants and animals:

1 **Plant:** grows close to the ground; short; rudimentary root system
  Animal: lots of fur; padded or hooved feet; light in color

2 **Plant:** Short, stubby leaves; wide, spreading roots; bulbous
  Animal: Light colored; short, close to ground; nocturnal

3 **Plant:** Long, long roots; wide leaves; prolific
  Animal: Amphibious; can live in water and on land; well-developed eyelids

4 **Plant:** Strong roots; broad leaves; close to ground
  Animal: Sheds skin; has scales; hibernates

Page 67

M Cardiologist
Tu The Northern Hemisphere is tilted away from the sun; the Southern Hemisphere is tilted toward the sun.
W 100 small calories
Th Plant life
F Australia

Page 68

1   Washington—active; California—inactive; Hawaii—active; Alaska—inactive; Oregon—inactive

2   Mount St. Helens, Washington, in the spring of 1980 (Other answers are possible.)
    a. Ash, steam, pieces of rock were thrown out of the volcano; the top of the mountain was blown off.
    b. Trees were leveled, animals were killed, some people were killed; many people had to move away from the area; a thick layer of ash covered the ground.
    c. Vegetation is growing again on the slopes; some animals are beginning to return; many people are visiting the area.

3   There are volcanoes in the Pacific "Ring of Fire": the Aleutian Islands, Mexico, Guatamala, El Salvador, Argentina, Colombia, Ecuador, Nicaragua, Chile, New Zealand, Papua New Guinea, Philippine Islands, Volcano Islands, Japan, U.S.S.R. Also in Canary Islands, Samoan Islands, Iceland, Lesser Antilles, Italy, Antarctica.

4   79 A.D. in Italy; Pompeii was buried by volcanic ash, mud, and pumice stone.

Page 69

M   Autumn
Tu The area of the Earth where the most volcanoes and earthquakes occur
W   1100 yards
Th Penguin, at the South Pole
F   High temperatures

Page 70

1   Weight on Jupiter would be 2.64 times the weight on Earth. Weight on Mars would be ⅓ times the weight on Earth.

2   15 pounds per square inch; atmospheric pressure on Venus is 90.5 times that on Earth; approximately 1,357.5 pounds of pressure per square inch on Venus. Atmospheric pressure on Mars is 99% less than that on Earth; approximately .15 pounds of pressure per square inch on Mars.

3   Earth and Venus
4   Earth and Mars
5   Earth and Mars
6   Earth, Venus, and Mars
7   Jupiter
8   Jupiter; Great Red Spot

Page 71

M   Warm and moist
Tu When the comet is moving away from the sun
W   Wood, spring, sun, coal, gasoline
Th

M													
A	M	P	H	I	B	I	A	N	S				
M						I							
M					R	E	P	T	I	L	E	S	
A					D								
L			F	I	S	H							
S													

F   Southern Hemisphere

Page 72

1   Los Angeles
2   Phoenix, Tucson
3   Denver
4   Seattle, Portland
5   Chicago
6   Boston
7   San Francisco, Seattle
8   New Orleans, Miami
9   Kansas City, Oklahoma City

THINK ABOUT IT! Science Problems of the Day   © 1993 Ideal School Supply Company